BIBLE 410
GOD'S WAY IS PERFECT

CONTENTS

Author:	Dolores Stedman, M.S.
Editor-in-Chief:	Richard W. Wheeler, M.A. Ed.
Editor:	Joyce Andrews Davis
Consulting Editor:	John L. Booth, Th.D.
Revision Editor:	Alan Christopherson, M.S.

Alpha Omega Publications ®

300 North McKemy Avenue, Chandler, Arizona 85226-2618

GOD'S WAY IS PERFECT

As for God, his way is perfect: the word of the LORD is tried: he is a buckler to all those that trust in him.
(Psalm 18:30)

Have you ever made cookies or a cake? If so, you know that you did not just throw anything into a bowl and stir it up. You put in just the right things at the right time. Cookies and cakes have to be made according to a plan.

The Bible tells of God's plan. He made the world; He planned for Jesus to be born, die, and rise again. He planned for Jesus to go back to heaven and prepare a place for us, and He plans for Jesus to come back again. Meanwhile, we have His Word to give us knowledge and understanding and to help us make wise choices.

During this year you have learned many things about God and His Word. We hope you have learned that God's way is the best way. God has a wonderful plan for your life. His way is perfect.

This LIFEPAC® is a review of what you have been learning in Bible this year.

OBJECTIVES

Read these objectives. The objectives tell you what you should be able to do when you have successfully completed this LIFEPAC.

When you have finished this LIFEPAC, you should be able to do the following:

1. Name the best way to receive God's knowledge.
2. Explain when and where to read the Bible.
3. Tell how and why we should memorize Scripture.
4. Tell how the Bible is superior to science.
5. Tell how geography affects people.
6. Explain how a person is born again into God's family.
7. Tell how God uses men to carry out His plans.
8. Identify God as the one who helps and protects us.
9. Explain why we should witness.
10. Describe Jesus' example of love.

VOCABULARY

Study these words. Knowing the meanings of these words will help you understand this LIFEPAC.

adopt (u dopt'). To take for one's own.

anoint (u noint'). To put oil on.

Canaan (kā' nun). The land of promise.

Epistle (i pis' ul). A letter that became a book of the Bible.

glorify (glôr' u fī). To praise, honor, and worship.

knowledge (nol' ij). What a person knows.

physical (fiz' u kul). Of the body.

principle (prin' su pul). A basic truth.

promise (prom' is). Words that say a person will do something.

spiritual (spir' u chù ul). Having to do with the spirit.

timeless (tīm' lis). Never ending.

Note: All vocabulary words in this LIFEPAC appear in **boldface** print the first time they are used. If you are unsure of the meaning when you are reading, study the definitions given.

Pronunciation Key: hat, āge, cãre, fär; let, ēqual, tėrm; it, īce; hot, ōpen, ôrder; oil; out; cup, pùt, rüle; child; long; thin; /ŦH/ for then; /zh/ for measure; /u/ represents /a/ in about, /e/ in taken, /i/ in pencil, /o/ in lemon, and /u/ in circus.

I. LEARNING GOD'S WAY

We can learn many things about God by just looking around us at His creation. The universe, the earth, and even our bodies tell us how wonderful and powerful He is.

However, the best place to learn about God is to read His Word. God wants us to know so many things. He shares His **knowledge** with us in His Word, the Bible.

In this section we will review how we can learn the things God wants us to know.

SECTION OBJECTIVES

Review these objectives. When you have completed this section, you should be able to:

1. Name the best way to receive God's knowledge.
2. Explain when and where to read the Bible.
3. Tell how and why we should memorize Scripture.
4. Tell how the Bible is superior to science.
5. Tell how geography affects people.

Restudy these words.

Canaan	principle	spiritual
knowledge	promise	timeless
physical		

Read Psalm 119:105 and John 1:18.

SEEKING KNOWLEDGE

How much do you know? You probably know more than you think you know. However, you still do not know nearly as much as God. God knows everything. All **knowledge** comes from Him.

God's knowledge is different from the knowledge of people. God's knowledge covers all situations and peoples. God always knows what is best. How can we learn of God's knowledge?

Where to find it. We can find out some things about God's knowledge just by looking at the things He made. He had to know very much to create the world and people. However, just looking at these things will not help us find out all that God wants us to know. God gave us the Bible so that we may learn of His knowledge.

One way God shared His knowledge was through His Son, Jesus. Jesus is the greatest teacher who ever lived. Learning from Jesus is learning from God, because Jesus is God. When you want to know what God thinks, read the words of Jesus in the Gospels.

Read these Bible verses.

1.1   The statement, *Jesus is God*, can be proved by reading John 14:9b and 10. Copy the verses on the lines exactly as they are written in the Bible.

_____

_____

_____

_____

_____

Do these puzzles.

1.2   Who was this man? Unscramble the letters and write his name on the line.

His name was _____ .

1.3   Color the dotted sections in the box to find out who he was.

He was a _____ .

King Solomon was given wisdom by God. First Kings 4:29 and 31 say, "And God gave Solomon wisdom and understanding exceeding much. ...For he was wiser than all men... and his fame was in all nations...."

Solomon wrote much of His wisdom and knowledge in the book of Proverbs. Proverbs are **principles**, or basic truths, God wants us to obey.

The **timeless** principles in the book of Proverbs are as important today as they were in the day God gave them to Solomon. Learning the Proverbs will help us gain knowledge and wisdom. Obeying God's proverbs will make us wise and happy. Take time to reread some of the Proverbs.

Read these Proverbs (15:1, 3:5, 18:15, 28:27, 2:6, 22:29, and 13:18). Circle the letter of the things you will do if you are wise. Write the Proverb reference on the line.

1.4   If you are wise you will

a. get understanding _____
b. trust in the Lord _____

c. gossip _____
d. give gentle answers _____

e. accept correction _____

f. always think you are right _____
g. work hard _____
h. do good to those that need it _____
i. believe anything _____
j. get knowledge _____

Write words to complete these sentences by adding a suffix to a root word from the Word Bank.

WORD BANK

Root Words		Suffixes	
great	king	er	est
joy	teach	less	ful
time	fast	ing	dom

1.5   Solomon's a. _____ was one of the b. _____ _____ because he was c. _____ God's ways.

1.6   If we obey the Proverbs, we can live _____ lives.

1.7   The principles taught in Proverbs are _____ .

How to apply it. Learning God's knowledge helps us in many ways. When we learn that God knows everything, we feel safe. God knows us so well that we can turn to Him for help.

God always knows what we are doing and what we are thinking. God knows how much we love Him. God knows us better than we know ourselves.

The Bible says (Proverbs 3:5), "Trust in the Lord with all thine heart; and lean not unto thine own understanding." We can ask God to give us His knowledge. The Holy Spirit will help us have understanding. When we pray, we should pause and think about God's Word. In this way we allow the things God is telling us in His Word to fill our minds and change us. God is pleased and blesses us when we seek His knowledge. We can have the knowledge of God. We can be wise if we will seek Him (Proverbs 2:1 through 9).

 Read these Bible verses and answer the questions *yes* **or** *no.*

Proverbs 23:13 and 14   Proverbs 29:15

1.8   Is it good for a child to always do as he chooses? _____

1.9   Should parents discipline their children when they disobey?_____

Rewrite each mixed-up word so you can read the sentences.

 odg si laspeed nehw ew esek sih wnokdglee.

_____

1.11   ska dog rof leegdwonk.

_____

Write three proverbs.

1.12   In Bible LIFEPAC 404 you memorized several Proverbs. How well do you remember them? Write three of them here from memory and then say them to your teacher.

a. _____

_____

_____

b. _____

_____

_____

c. _____

_____

_____

Teacher check _____
                       Initial   Date

Read 2 Timothy 2:15 and 3:16.

STUDYING THE BIBLE

Studying the Bible means reading it and learning what God wants us to know. As we are learning, we will be thinking about God. Success in the Christian life depends on how much of the Bible we get into our minds and attitudes and how well we obey it.

The Bible is no ordinary book. The Bible is life changing. Everything we need to know about God is found in the Bible. Everything we need to know about being a Christian and living a Christian life is found in the Bible.

Start by reading. Daily Bible reading is to our **spiritual** life what daily eating is to our **physical** life.

Most people find morning to be the best time to read the Bible. We must find a quiet place we can be alone. It is best to sit up at a desk or table to read.

We should begin our Bible study with prayer, asking God to help us learn something from Him.

Write the letter of the correct answer on the line.

1.13   Everything we need to know about God is found _____ .
        a. in the Bible
        b. in our minds

1.14   Daily Bible reading helps our _____ .
        a. spiritual life
        b. physical life

1.15   When we read our Bible, it is best to _____ .
        a. lie down
        b. sit up

1.16   God used _____ to write the book of Proverbs.
        a. David
        b. Solomon

1.17   The book of Proverbs contains many _____ .
        a. wise sayings
        b. stories

1.18   Solomon was very _____ .
        a. wise
        b. lazy

1.19   When you want to know what God thinks, _____ .
        a. ask Him for a dream
        b. read the Bible

1.20   God is happy when we _____ .
        a. seek His knowledge
        b. do things our way

Three things you should look for, are **promises**, commands, and if you expect to learn from the Bible, principles.

Often when a promise is given, God asks us to obey Him first. When we read a promise, we must ask ourselves, "Do I have to do something before God will do something?" Then read before and after the promise to see what you must do. In Second Chronicles 7:14 God promises to forgive sin and heal the land. However, that same verse says that His people have to humble themselves, pray, seek His face, and turn from their wicked ways first. God will do as He promised if we will do what He asks.

The Bible has many commands for God's people to obey. Commands tell us what to do or not to do. Bible commands are for our good. If we obey them, our lives will be happier and successful.

The Bible has timeless principles. Principles are ideas from God that help us. If these ideas get into our minds, we will make wise choices.

 Complete this activity.

1.21 Three things we should look for in the Bible are
a. _____ , b. _____ ,
and c. _____ .

Match these words and phrases.

1.22 _____   tell you what to do or   a. principles
what not to do

1.23 _____   timeless ideas from   b. commands
God

1.24 _____   often ask you to do   c. promises
something before God
will do something

Read these Bible verses and answer the questions.

Colossians 2:3	John 13:17	Proverbs 3:6
Proverbs 2:6	Proverbs 3:5	Proverbs 1:7

1.25   Which verse commands us to trust the Lord and not our own understanding? _____

1.26   Which verse says that from God comes knowledge and understanding? _____

1.27   Which verse calls God's wisdom and knowledge a treasure?

      _____

1.28   Which verse promises that the Lord will direct our paths?

      _____

1.29   Which verse says that the fear of the Lord is the beginning of knowledge? _____

1.30   Which verse says we will be happy if we follow God's principles? _____

1.31   Proverbs 3:6 is a promise. What must we do first before God will keep His promise? _____

Work on memorizing. Memorizing Scripture will help us grow. Memorizing the Bible will take some work, but it will help us grow into strong Christians.

Knowing Scripture helps us not to sin. It also helps us not to be afraid. Knowing God's Word helps us to be more like Jesus and gives us understanding of what we believe.

When we know God's Word, we can share our love for God with others by telling them what the Bible says. These words remind us how to memorize Scripture:

COPY
READ
SAY
TELL
RESTUDY

 Complete these statements by using each word correctly.

love	Jesus	afraid
sin	understand	

1.32   Memorizing God's Word will
a. help you have victory over _____ ,
b. help you not to be _____ ,
c. help you share your _____ for God,
d. help you be more like _____ , and
e. help you _____ what you believe.

Write *true* **or** *false.*

1.33 _____ Learning from Jesus is the same as learning from God.

1.34 _____ All true knowledge comes from God.

1.35 _____ Proverbs are principles, or basic truths, God wants us to obey.

1.36 _____ We should never ask God for knowledge.

1.37 _____ The Holy Spirit helps us understand God's Word.

1.38 _____ Bible commands are not always for our good.

1.39 _____ The steps for memorizing Scripture are copy, read, say, tell, restudy.

EXAMINING SCIENCE

The Bible is not a science book, but when the Bible talks about things of science, it has been proved to be correct. Not once has the Bible been found to be wrong.

The Bible tells us about the universe, our earth, and our bodies. Science also has much to say about these things.

The universe. How did our universe begin? This question has been asked by many people. Scientists have tried hard to explain the key of the universe. Some people think the universe just happened because they do not believe the Bible. Science has many theories. Do you remember some of them?

The Bible tells us very simply that God made the universe and is looking over it right now. Read Isaiah 45:12.

Answer this question.

1.40   Does science know how many stars are in the sky? _____

Write *true* **or** *false.*

1.41   _____   The Bible is a science book.
1.42   _____   Sometimes the Bible is wrong.

1.43 _____ Many men think the universe just happened.

1.44 _____ The Bible tells us that God made the universe.

The earth. God used His knowledge to create the earth. He carefully planned it. The earth did not just happen. He spoke and His words created it.

Yet, many scientists say they do not know how the earth got here. They say God did not make it. It must have just happened.

Many scientists think that millions of years ago a tiny thing, too small to see, suddenly became alive and began to grow. It was not God who made it come alive they say, because to them there is no God. Although they are wise in some ways, these scientists are very foolish when it comes to believing what God says.

The Bible has much information about our earth. You probably remember many of these things from Bible LIFEPACs 402 and 406. These things were recorded long before scientists even began to study the earth. How did the Bible writers know so much? God told them what to write.

 Read Genesis 1:1–2:3.

1.45 Number the sentences in the order they happened according to the Bible.

a. _____ God created man in His own image.

b. _____ God created day and night.

c. _____ God gathered the waters together to make dry land. God made plant life.

d. _____ God rested from His work.

e. _____ God made the sun, moon, and the stars.

f. _____ God made the firmament.

g. _____ God made the birds and animals.

Our bodies. Scientists have learned much about the human body. They have even tried to make a human body, but failed. They have been able to make some body parts, but they are only copies of the ones God has made.

The greatest wonder of all creation is the human body. God planned it carefully. He made each person in a special way and each person is different. You body is proof that God lives.

Why did God make us? God made us to glorify Him and to enjoy Him. God wants us to thank Him for being so good to us. He wants us to worship Him by loving Him in return for what He has done for us.

A very smart man, named Aquinas, lived hundreds of years ago. He often thought about God. Thomas Aquinas wrote laws to tell that God exists.

 Review Colossians 1:16 and Psalm 100:3 and write the missing words.

1.46 "For by him were a. _____ things created, that are in b. _____ , and that are in c. _____ , visible and invisible, whether they be d. _____ , or dominions, or principalities, or powers: all things were created by e. _____ , and f. _____ him." (Colossians 1:16)

1.47 "Know ye that the a. _____ he is b. _____ : it is he that hath c. _____ us and not we ourselves; we are his d. _____ , and the e. _____ of his pasture." (Psalm 100:3)

Answer these questions.

1.48 How did the Bible writers of long ago know about things before the scientists did? _____

1.49 Why did God make us? _____

_____

Write *true* **or** *false.*

1.50 _____ God is pleased when we seek His knowledge.

1.51 _____ We should read the Bible about once a month.

1.52 _____ God used Joseph to write the book of Proverbs.

14

1.53	_____	The book of Proverbs is a history book.
1.54	_____	Commands tell us what to do or what not to do.
1.55	_____	Memorizing God's Word will help give us victory over sin.
1.56	_____	If we memorize verses from the Bible, we will have no more problems.

 Do this activity.

1.57 Read Genesis, Chapters 1 and 2. In one minute write on this flower as many things as you can think of that God created. Have a friend help you. When he says, "Go," begin.

 Read Psalm 90.

UNDERSTANDING GEOGRAPHY

This year you learned about the geography of the lands that are part of Bible events. Studying Bible geography is important because it helps us understand the way the people of Bible lands lived. The land of the Bible was, and still is, important.

In Bible times this land was called **Canaan**. Today we refer to this area as the Holy Land. God chose Canaan to play an important part in world history.

Why study Bible lands? Geography is the study of land and what is on it. The reason we studied Bible geography this year was to understand Bible-land customs and to learn the setting for the events written about in the Bible.

Customs are the ways people do things. A setting is where an event takes place.

The land, climate, and water all help to decide how people will live. God is in control of these things. The kind of weather and land He gave His people were all part of His purpose. God has a purpose in putting you where you are, too.

☞ **Complete these statements.**

1.58   Two reasons we studied Bible geography this year are

a. _____ and

b. _____ .

1.59   A word that means *ways people do things* is _____ .

1.60   A word that means *where an event takes place* is _____ .

What the Bible lands were like. Most of the events of the Bible took place in what we call the Holy Land. This land was called Canaan in Bible times.

From north to south, it is only about 150 miles (240 kilometers). From east to west, Canaan is only about 100 miles (160 kilometers) at its widest point. Canaan is only a little larger than the state of New Jersey in the United States.

As you read the Bible, you will notice that rivers are often mentioned. Because this land is mainly desert, rivers are important for farming. The three main rivers are the Tigris, the Euphrates, and the Jordan.

The area around the rivers is the shape of a crescent, or new moon. The soil around the rivers is richer and more fertile than in other areas. This area, called the Fertile Crescent, is where farming is done.

Much of Canaan is rocky and hilly. Stones are plentiful, so many houses are built with stones. The Holy Land has tall mountains and areas below sea level, fertile farmland and waterless deserts, and windy, cold areas and hot, dry places.

The Holy Land has many different climates.

Many people crossed this area as they traveled. The lands of Bible times were important centers of trade and business.

 Do this puzzle.

1.61 Unscramble the words and write the names of the three rivers of Bible lands in the boxes.

SIRITG
DRJONA
AESPEHRUT

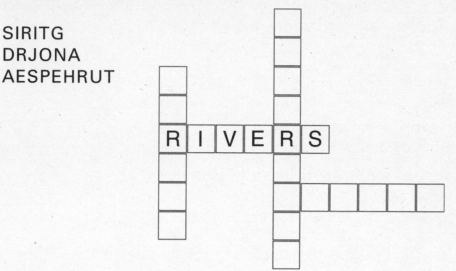

R I V E R S

 Do this map activity.

1.62 Trace the rivers in blue. The shaded area is the Fertile Crescent. Color the Fertile Crescent green.

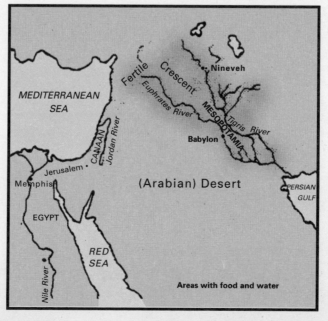

 Teacher check _____

Write *true* **or** *false.*

1.63 _____ The Holy Land is about the size of Texas.

1.64 _____ Land watered by rivers will grow much food.

1.65 _____ *Fertile* means *bare.*

1.66 _____ Deserts are almost waterless.

1.67 _____ Customs of the people in the Bible are different from ours.

1.68 _____ The climate of the Bible lands includes very cold and very hot climates.

Complete these activities.

1.69 Write each word in syllables.

a. important _____   d. mountains _____

b. fertile _____   e. Bible _____

c. crescent _____   f. Tigris _____

1.70 Review Genesis 12:2 and write the missing words.

"And I will make of thee a a. _____ nation, and I will b. _____ thee, and make thy name c. _____ ; and thou shalt be a d. _____ ." (Genesis 12:2)

1.71 To whom is God speaking in this verse? _____

Review the material in this section to prepare for the Self Test. The Self Test will check your understanding of this section. Any items you miss on this test will show you what areas you need to restudy.

SELF TEST 1

Match these items (each answer, 3 points).

1.01 _____	Proverbs	a. good people
1.02 _____	timeless	b. wise saying
1.03 _____	fertile	c. rich soil
1.04 _____	geography	d. almost waterless
1.05 _____	desert	f. no beginning nor end
1.06 _____	Canaan	g. Holy Land
		h. study of earth and what is on it

Write the letter of the correct answer on the line (each answer, 4 points).

1.07   The best way to find God's knowledge is by _____ .
   a. going to college
   b. reading your Bible
   c. asking a friend

1.08   A way to receive knowledge from God is to _____ .
   a. sit under a tree
   b. look at the stars
   c. study His Word

1.09   Begin Bible study with _____ .
   a. prayer
   b. a glass of milk
   c. a good book

1.010   God's principles are _____ .
   a. basic truths
   b. a story
   c. Psalms

1.011   Bible writers knew things before scientists discovered them
   because _____ .
   a. they studied rocks
   b. they read a lot
   c. God told them

1.012   Thomas Aquinas wrote laws to prove that _____ .
                a. water flows downhill
                b. God exists
                c. man is wise

1.013   The greatest wonder God created is _____ .
                a. the sun
                b. the oceans
                c. the human body

1.014   Memorizing Scripture will help you not to be _____ .
                a. happy
                b. an adult
                c. afraid

1.015   The steps for memorizing Scripture are _____ .
                a. copy, read, say, tell, restudy
                b. read, tell, restudy, copy, say

Write *true* **or** *false* (each answer, 3 points).

1.016 _____ Scientists can make a human body.

1.017 _____ David wrote the book of Proverbs.

1.018 _____ Many Bible promises ask you to obey God first.

1.019 _____ Commands tell you what to do or what not to do.

1.020 _____ We study Bible geography to understand the customs and the settings of the Bible people.

Write a correct word from the list to complete each sentence (each answer, 4 points).

         physical   God
         Genesis   Scripture
         Matthew   mental
         sin   knowledge
         spiritual   work

1.021   Daily Bible reading is to your a. _____ life what daily eating is to your b. _____ life.

1.022   Memorizing _____ will help you tell others about Jesus.

1.023   Only _____ can make life.

1.024   Memorizing Scripture will help you not to _____ .

1.025   The book in the Bible that tells the story of Creation is

_____ .

1.026   God shares His _____ through His Word.

Do one of these things (this answer, 3 points).

1.027   a. Write a Bible verse that tells about God's knowledge and
          tell where the verse is found in the Bible.

         b. Write a Bible verse that tells us that God created all things
          and tell where the verse is found in the Bible.

         c. Write a Proverb and tell where it is found in the Bible.

_____

_____

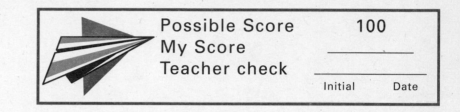

Possible Score		100
My Score		_____
Teacher check		_____
	Initial	Date

II. LIVING GOD'S WAY

The most important thing in life is to obey God and to live His way. When you live God's way, it makes Him happy. When you live God's way, you are happy also.

The Holy Spirit can help us want to live God's way. In this section we will review how we can live God's way. We will review the lives of some great men of God. We will see how they believed in Jesus, walked in the Spirit, and trusted in God.

SECTION OBJECTIVES

Review these objectives. When you have completed this section, you should be able to:

6. Explain how a person is born again into God's family.
7. Tell how God used men to carry out His plan.
8. Identify God as the one who helps and protects us.

Read John 1:28–44.

BELIEVING IN JESUS

I tried to walk upon the sea, Jesus said, "Now just trust me." I sank and said, "Help, or I'll die!" Jesus did it—why couldn't I?

Who am I? _____

At first Simon wasn't sure what Andrew, his brother, was so excited about. "Simon, please come and meet Jesus!" he kept saying. So Simon went with his brother to see Jesus.

When they returned to their home, Simon was the one who was the most excited. "Jesus gave me a new name," said Simon. "My new name is Peter, which means a stone."

Peter believes in Jesus. Peter and his brother, Andrew, both became followers (disciples) of Jesus. They were with Jesus every day, seeing His miracles and hearing His teachings.

Peter saw Jesus take five loaves and two fishes and feed over five thousand people. He saw the blind receive their sight and deaf men hear. He saw people raised from the dead.

One time Jesus helped Peter walk on water. But Peter became frightened, took his eyes off Jesus, and started to sink. Jesus had to help him back into the boat.

Jesus taught about forgiveness and many other Biblical principles. Peter learned many lessons from Jesus. One day Jesus washed the feet of His disciples. This act seemed very strange to Peter.

Peter was there when Jesus was taken away and killed, but after Jesus arose Peter saw Him several times. After Jesus went back to heaven, the Holy Spirit was given on the Day of Pentecost. Peter was empowered to preach.

Peter spent the rest of his life preaching and telling others the

Gospel, or "good news," about Jesus. Peter believed that Jesus was God's son and the Savior of the world. Peter lived hundreds of years ago, but people today are still believing in Jesus.

Draw the story.

2.1   Draw a picture in each box to go with the sentences.

a. Andrew invites Simon to go see Jesus. Andrew is excited.	b. They return home. Simon is excited. Jesus gave me a new name!
c. Peter and Andrew both become followers of Jesus.	d. They saw Jesus do many miracles. (draw one)
e. They saw Jesus after He was killed and rose again.	f. Peter spent his life preaching the "good news" or the "Gospel."

Teacher check _____
                    Initial   Date

You can believe in Jesus. As we know, God's way is perfect. God had a perfect plan. He sent His Son to die for our sins. God prepared a body for His Son so that He would be like us. Jesus was born, lived on earth, died, and rose again.

Did God punish Jesus because of His own sins? No, Jesus had no sin. Jesus came to die for our sins. Jesus came to be our Savior from sin.

Have you asked Jesus to be your Savior? Are you part of God's family? Our physical selves were born into an earthly family. Our spiritual selves need to be born into a heavenly family. The heavenly family is the family of God. We are born into God's family when we ask Jesus to come into our life and cleanse us from sin.

If you have not asked Jesus to be your Savior, you can ask Him right now. Just bow your head and pray. Ask Jesus to come into your life and make you His child or ask your teacher to pray with you.

Do this activity.

2.2   Write the missing letters on the bells. The bells will spell the word that means "good news."

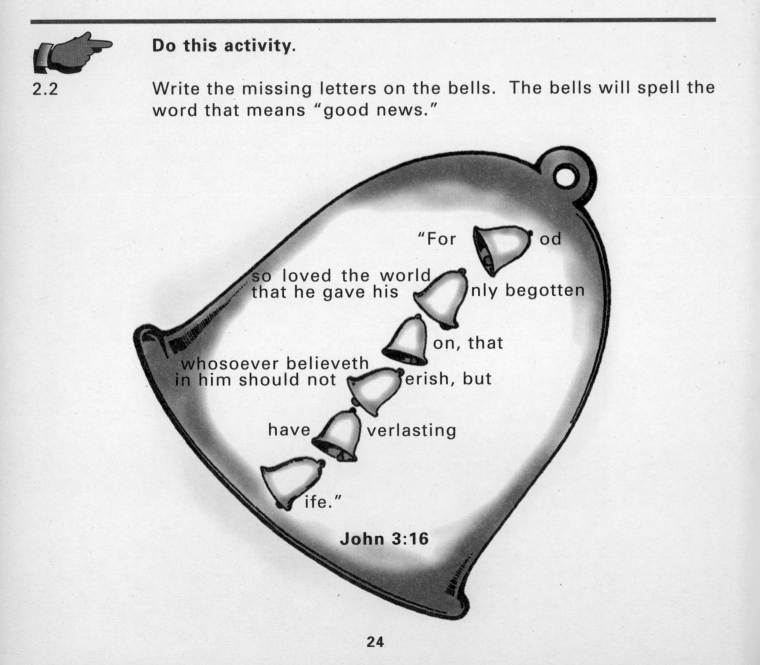

"For ☐ od so loved the world that he gave his ☐ nly begotten ☐ on, that whosoever believeth in him should not ☐ erish, but have ☐ verlasting ☐ ife."

John 3:16

BIBLE

410

LIFEPAC TEST

$\dfrac{80}{100}$

Name _____

Date _____

Score _____

BIBLE 410: LIFEPAC TEST

Match these items (each answer, 2 points).

1.	_____	Canaan	a. a wise saying
2.	_____	Proverb	b. followers of Jesus
3.	_____	disciples	c. Holy Land
4.	_____	witness	d. good news
5.	_____	Gospel	e. to take for one's own
6.	_____	adopt	f. love others
			g. tell what you know

Write *true* **or** *false* (each answer, 2 points).

7. _____ Settings are places where happenings take place.

8. _____ *Fertile* means *bare.*

9. _____ Geography does not tell much about people.

10. _____ Canaan was about the size of Texas.

11. _____ The Fertile Crescent is where farming was done.

12. _____ Commands tell us what to do.

13. _____ We will be happy if we obey what God tells us in the Bible.

14. _____ Memorizing Scripture will help you not to sin.

15. _____ Peter's brother brought him to Jesus.

16. _____ Good works will get us to heaven.

17. _____ Believe in yourself, and you can do anything.

18. _____ My worth comes from God.

Complete these sentences by writing the letter and answer on the blank (each answer, 3 points).

19. In Bible times the Holy Land was called _____ .
   a. Canaan
   b. Egypt
   c. United States

1

20.   The greatest wonder of all God's creation is _____ .
        a. the earth
        b. the human body
        c. the ocean

21.   Jesus came to earth to save people from their _____ .
        a. worries
        b. friends
        c. sins

22.   The book of Proverbs was written mostly by _____ .
        a. Solomon
        b. David
        c. Paul

23.   If we obey God's principles, we will be _____ .
        a. sad
        b. fat
        c. happy

24.   The story of Creation is written in the book of _____ .
        a. Acts
        b. Genesis
        c. Proverbs

25.   You can learn God's knowledge by _____ .
        a. reading the Bible
        b. going to college
        c. studying science

26.   The writer of the Twenty-Third Psalm is _____ .
        a. Paul
        b. David
        c. Solomon

Complete these sentences with words from the list (each answer, 3 points).

spiritual	Colossians 3:20	Philippians 4:13	Mark 16:15
Psalm 23	Psalm 100:3	Bible	timeless
Epistles	physical	commands	Proverbs 23
mental	Paul	retell	people
Jesus	God	restudy	knowledge

27.   The Bible writers were told what to write by _____ .

28.   God speaks to us through the _____ .

29.   Daily Bible reading is to your a. _____ life
       what daily eating is to your b. _____ life.

30.   We know what to do or what not to do by God's _____ .

31.   The steps of memorizing Scripture are copy, read, say, tell
       and _____ .

32.   The Good Shepherd is _____ .

33.   The letters Paul wrote to the churches are called _____
       _____ .

34.   "The Lord is my shepherd" is found in _____ .

35.   "I can do all things through Christ ..." is found in
       _____ .

Complete these Bible verses (each answer, 5 points).

36.   "Know ye that the Lord he is God: it is he that hath made us
       and not we ourselves; _____
       _____ ." (Psalm 100:3)

37.   "Go ye _____
       _____ ." (Mark 16:15)

Review this Bible verse. Write the missing words on the lines and then say it to a friend without looking.

2.3   "But as many as a. _____ Him, to them gave
        He b. _____ to become the c. _____
        of d. _____ , even to them that e. _____
        on his name." (John 1:12)

        Friend check _____
                                    name

Write the word for each definition given. One letter in each word has been written for you.

2.4   The study of the earth
        and what is on it is __ __ __ __ R __ __ __ __ .
2.5   God's principles are __ __ __ E __ __ __ __ .
2.6   A wise saying is a __ __ __ V __ __ __ .
2.7   Memorizing Scripture will help you not to __ I __ .
2.8   The story of Creation is found in __ __ __ E __ __ __ .
2.9   God wants us to seek His __ __ __ W __ __ __ __ __ .

Complete these sentences with words from the list.

        hurt   Jesus   sin
        Son   died   us

2.10   God sent Jesus, His only _____ , to earth.
2.11   Jesus _____ for our sins.
2.12   Jesus had no _____ of His own.
2.13   All men need _____ .

WALKING IN THE SPIRIT

A bright light shown down on me. For a long time I could not see. Then Jesus spoke and I answered too,

"Lord, what wilt Thou have me do?

Who am I? _____

Saul was known as the cruelest enemy of Christians. He put them in prison or had them killed. Saul thought Christians were telling a lie when they said Jesus was alive.

Saul is saved. Saul and his group were on their way to Damascus to kill Christians when suddenly a bright light from heaven shone down. Saul fell to the ground. Jesus spoke to Saul and told him to go into the city and there he would be told what to do. Saul was blinded so his friends had to lead him.

Saul had a kind of dream. In his dream Ananias put his hands on him and Saul was able to see again. At the same time God was preparing Ananias to visit Saul. Ananias was afraid, but he obeyed God. He did exactly as God had told him and Saul was able to see again. Saul was filled with the Holy Spirit and was baptized. Later Saul's name was changed to Paul.

 **Complete this activity.**

2.14 Six incorrect words are in these sentences. Cross each one out and print the correct homonym above it. The first one is done for you.

daze
Paul walked to Damascus in a ~~days~~. He new the Sun of God had spoken to hymn. He was thinking about what he wood due.

26

Complete this puzzle.

2.15   You can go along with Paul from Jerusalem to Damascus by going through the letter maze in the correct order. Draw a line beginning at Jerusalem through the words that are exactly like those an Acts 9:3.

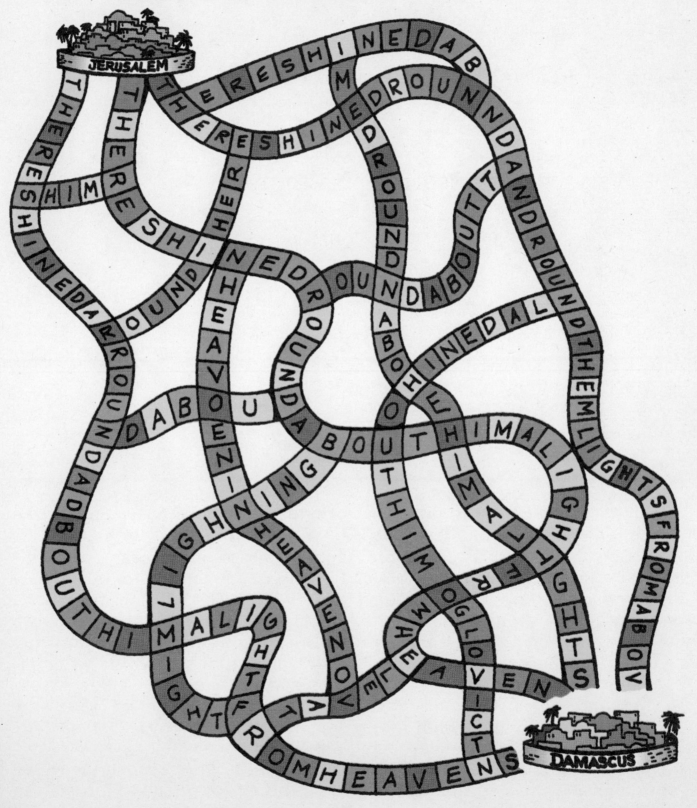

Answer these questions.

2.16   Why did Saul hurt Christians? _____

2.17   How did Jesus prove to Saul that He was alive? _____
_____

2.18   The story of Saul meeting Jesus is found in what book of the
Bible? _____

2.19   What blinded Saul? _____

Read 1 Corinthians 15:3 and 4, and complete this verse.

2.20   "THAT CHRIST a. _____

FOR OUR SINS ACCORDING TO THE

SCRIPTURES; AND THAT HE WAS

b. _____ ,   AND THAT HE

c. _____   AGAIN THE d. _____

DAY ACCORDING TO THE   e. _____ ."

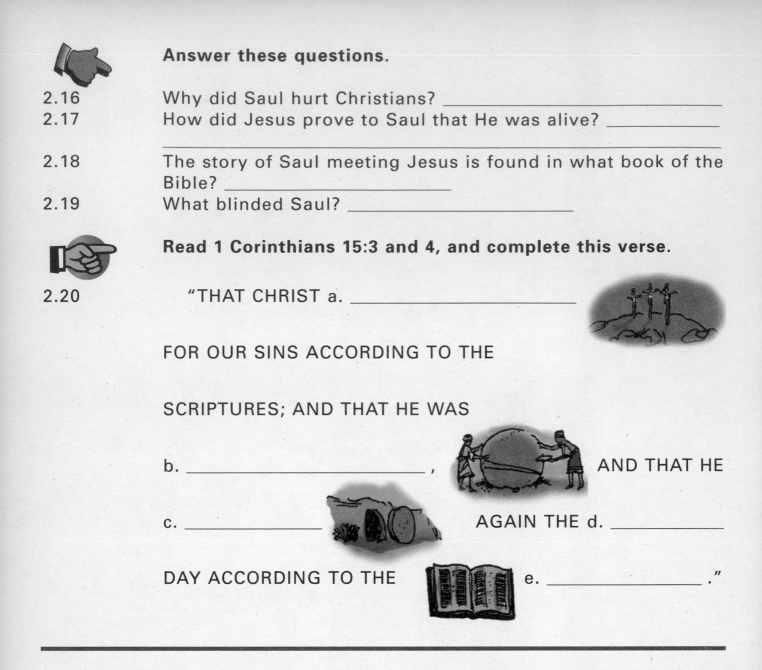

Paul lives for God. Right away Paul began to preach that Jesus was God's Son. He surprised people. The very man who had been killing Christians was now one of them. Soon the Jewish leaders made up a plan to kill Paul. The Christians had to put him in a basket and let him down over the city wall so that he could escape.

The Holy Spirit taught Paul more about Jesus and what God expects of His followers. After that Paul made many exciting trips to tell others what the Holy Spirit had taught Him. He helped start churches in many places.

Paul wrote letters to these new churches. We call the letters he wrote **Epistles**. Paul also wrote letters to certain people. The Holy Spirit gave him the words to write. Some of the letters that Paul wrote later became books of the New Testament. Paul wrote thirteen New Testament books.

Paul suffered because he lived and worked for Jesus. Paul said in

28

Romans 8:35 through 39 that nothing would keep him from loving Jesus or Jesus from loving him.

Are you living for God? The Holy Spirit worked in Paul's life to help him become more like Jesus. The Holy Spirit will work in your life, too, to make you more like Jesus.

If you study the Bible, the Holy Spirit will help you learn God's principles. You will learn how important it is to obey your parents and to be a good friend as you live with other people.

As you study God's Word, the Holy Spirit will give you wisdom and knowledge. You will learn to live the Bible way, which is God's perfect way.

You should already know that you cannot work your way to heaven. Only those who receive Jesus into their heart can go to heaven. However, you will find that you want to work for Jesus, as Paul did, because you love Him.

 Write *true* **or** *false.*

2.21 _____ Paul wrote thirteen New Testament books.

2.22 _____ We can work for our salvation.

2.23 _____ Salvation is a gift from God.

2.24 _____ We should work for Jesus because we love Him.

2.25 _____ Paul helped start many new churches.

2.26 _____ Paul began to preach that Jesus was the Son of God right after Peter laid hands on him.

 Circle the letter of the correct sentence in each pair of sentences.

2.27   a. The Jewish leaders planned to kill Paul.
         b. The Jewish leaders planned to honor Paul.

2.28   a. Paul helped to start many churches.
         b. Paul wrote letters to churches only.

2.29   a. Paul wrote eighteen books in the New Testament.
         b. Paul wrote thirteen books in the New Testament.

2.30   a. Memorizing Scripture will help you not to be young.
         b. Memorizing scripture will help you not to be afraid.

2.31   a. The story of Saul meeting Jesus is found in Acts.
        b. The story of Saul meeting Jesus is found in Mark.

 Write the answers to these questions.

2.32   What could you do if your class were acting very badly?

_____

_____

_____

_____

2.33   What could you do if your mother needs your help?

_____

_____

_____

_____

 Read Psalm 23.

TRUSTING IN GOD

I prayed to God night and day
And in a lion's den did stay,
God was with me and let me out
I trust in Him and never doubt.
Who am I? _____

When you think of me you think of sheep.
I watched them as a boy.
When I grew up and became the king
I wrote some Psalms of joy.
Who am I? _____

Two men trust God. Daniel loved the Lord even when he had to stand alone. The story of Daniel tells how God has power over man and beast. Daniel was true to God and prayed even when it was against the law. As a result he was thrown into a den of lions. However, God kept Daniel safe. Daniel trusted God!

As a boy David had a special job to do. He took care of his father's sheep. God helped David kill a lion and a bear to protect his sheep. Later God also helped him kill Goliath and win the battle. David trusted God! You can read all about David in First and Second Samuel.

Answer these questions.

2.34   Who protected Daniel and David?_____

2.35   Do you think Daniel and David were thankful to God?_____

2.36   Has God ever protected you from danger or harm?_____

2.37   Have you thanked God for protecting you?_____

Complete this puzzle.

2.38   Color all the letters that appear five times in this puzzle. The letters that are left will spell something David said.

T	H	B	A	F	E	N	F	L	V	Z	O	Z	R	D	A	I
F	N	S	V	B	M	V	Z	Y	Z	A	S	F	N	H	A	B
E	Z	P	B	V	H	N	F	E	A	N	R	V	B	D		

2.39   Write David's words on this line. _____

The Twenty-Third Psalm. The Twenty-third Psalm is about just two people, the Lord and the believer. David wrote this wonderful Psalm. Since he had been a shepherd boy himself, he knew many things about sheep. If you have not read this Psalm lately make sure you stop and read it now.

Let us quickly review the meaning of these verses.

Psalm 23, Verse 1. A shepherd chooses and buys his sheep. The sheep are his after he pays for them. The Lord Jesus chose us and paid for us with His life. Now we are His. He wants to lead us. He gives us all we need.

Psalm 23, Verse 2. The shepherd's job is to see that the sheep have plenty to eat and drink. The green pastures and still waters stand for God's Word, the Bible, which is food and drink for our spiritual lives.

Psalm 23, Verse 3. The shepherd is always in front leading his sheep. He is never behind driving them. When a sheep wanders away, the shepherd searches for him and brings him back to safety. The "Good Shepherd," the Lord Jesus, leads His people the same way.

Psalm 23, Verse 4. In the dark valleys between the mountains are many dangers. The sheep are not afraid. They know their shepherd is just ahead, leading and protecting them.

If wild animals attack, the shepherd hits them with his rod. If a sheep goes off the path, the shepherd puts the crook of his staff around it and brings it back. Jesus wants His children to trust Him like the sheep trust the shepherd.

Psalm 23, Verse 5. David wrote that God prepares a table. We can think of God's Word as the food on the table for us.

As the sheep go into the fold at night, the shepherd looks for hurts. The shepherd **anoints**, or bathes, the bruises with oil. The Lord Jesus carefully watches us, too. When we have hard times and bad hurts, the Holy Spirit is there comforting us.

Psalm 23, Verse 6. In this verse David wrote of goodness and mercy following him. Where the "Good Shepherd" is, goodness and mercy will always be there. David also spoke of dwelling in the house of the Lord forever—forever in the company of the Lord, the Good Shepherd. The shepherd never stops watching his sheep. Jesus Christ, our shepherd, never stops watching us. He never sleeps.

Write the missing words.

2.40   "The a. _____ is my b. _____ ; I shall not
c. _____ . He maketh me to lie down in green
d._____ : he leadeth me beside the still
e. _____ . He restoreth my f. _____ : he leadeth me
in the g. _____ of righteousness for His name's sake.
Yea, though I walk through the h. _____ of the shadow
of i. _____ , I will fear no evil: for thou art with j. _____ ;
thy rod and thy k. _____ they comfort me. Thou
preparest a l. _____ before me in the presence of mine
m. _____ : thou anointest my n. _____ with oil;
my o. _____ runneth over. Surely p. _____
and q. _____ shall follow me all the days of my life: and
I will dwell in the r. _____ of the Lord for s. _____ ."

33

Memorize Psalm 23.

2.41   Learn Psalm 23. Use the method of study we reviewed in Section One. Say it perfectly to your teacher.

Teacher check _____
                    Initial   Date

Help the shepherd get his sheep into the fold by matching an answer sheep with each statement. Circle the sheep and write its answer on the line beside the correct statement. When all the sheep are circled the shepherd's job is done.

2.42   the "Good Shepherd" _____
2.43   wrote the Twenty-Third Psalm _____
2.44   prayed when it was against the law _____
2.45   trust the shepherd _____
2.46   should trust the Lord _____
2.47   means to *bathe with oil* _____
2.48   wrote most of the Proverbs _____
2.49   what to do or what not to do _____
2.50   wrote laws about God _____
2.51   the Holy Land _____
2.52   wise saying _____

34

2.53   Simon _____

2.54   saw a light from heaven _____

2.55   learning _____

2.56   invited Peter to meet Jesus _____

2.57   "Good News" _____

2.58   green pastures and still waters for the Christian

      _____

Review the material in this section to prepare for the Self Test. The Self Test will check your understanding of this section. Any items you miss on this test will show you what areas you need to restudy.

SELF TEST 2

Put these events in the correct order (each answer, 1 point).

2.01 _____   Saul asks Jesus what He wants him to do.

2.02 _____   A bright light shines on Saul.

2.03 _____   Paul suffers for Jesus.

2.04 _____   Saul hurts Christians because he thinks they are wrong.

2.05 _____   Paul tells others about Jesus.

2.06 _____   Saul is filled with the Holy Spirit.

Write the correct word on each line (each answer, 3 points).

2.07   "The Lord is my shepherd; I shall not a. _____ . He maketh me to lie down in green b. _____ : he leadeth me beside the still c. _____ . He restoreth my d. _____ : he leadeth me in the paths of e. _____ for his name's sake. Yea, though I walk through the valley of the shadow of f. _____ , I will fear no evil: for thou art with me; thy rod and thy g. _____ they comfort me. Thou preparest a h. _____ before me in the presence of mine enemies: thou anointest my head with i. _____ ; my j. _____ runneth over. Surely goodness and k. _____ shall follow me all the days of my life: and I will dwell in the house of the Lord for ever." (Psalm 23)

Match these words and names (each answer, 2 points).

2.08	_____	Simon
2.09	_____	a river
2.010	_____	prayed for Paul
2.011	_____	trusted God in the lions' den
2.012	_____	brought his brother to Jesus
2.013	_____	the Good Shepherd
2.014	_____	wrote Proverbs
2.015	_____	wrote Psalm 23
2.016	_____	wrote many Epistles

a. Paul
b. Solomon
c. Peter
d. David
e. Jordan
f. Andrew
g. Ananias
h. Daniel
i. Jesus
j. John

Write the letter of the answer that completes each sentence (each answer, 3 points).

2.017   The Holy Spirit changed Saul from an enemy of Christ to a
_____ of Christ.
a. follower
b. persecutor
c. rabbi

2.018   The letters Paul wrote to churches and people were called
_____ .
a. Apostles
b. Epistles
c. Testaments

2.019   Before Peter met Jesus his name was _____ .
a. Paul
b. Jonas
c. Simon

2.020   David wrote _____ .
a. Psalm 23
b. the book of Acts
c. Genesis

2.021   *Gospel* means _____ .
a. go and tell
b. good news
c. love

2.022   The story of Saul meeting Jesus is found in _____ .
                   a. Luke
                   b. Mark
                   c. Acts

2.023   Memorizing Scripture will help you not to _____ .
                   a. talk
                   b. laugh
                   c. sin

2.024   We were all born into an earthly family, but we need to be born again into a _____ .
                   a. heavenly family
                   b. mental family
                   c. rich family

2.025   The shepherd of the Twenty-Third Psalm is _____ .
                   a. Paul
                   b. Peter
                   c. Jesus

Write *true* **or** *false.* (each answer, 2 points).

2.026 _____ We study Bible geography to understand the customs of the people and the setting for the events of the Bible.

2.027 _____ You do not have to do anything to receive Bible promises.

2.028 _____ Scientists can make a human body.

2.029 _____ God's principles are timeless and are good for today.

2.030 _____ God's principles are basic truths.

2.031 _____ The best way to find God's knowledge is to ask a friend.

2.032 _____ A proverb is a story.

2.033 _____ Bible writers knew some things before scientists discovered them.

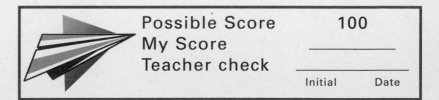

Possible Score	100
My Score	_____
Teacher check	_____
	Initial Date

III. LOVING GOD'S WAY

Loving the way God does is not easy. Loving takes the power of the Holy Spirit working in our lives. The more you love others the easier it becomes. If you take music lessons or play sports, you know how much practice it takes to do well. We need to practice when it comes to loving, also. We must learn to accept ourselves the way God made us and then love others the way God made them.

The Bible tells us many times that loving other people is one of the most important things in life. How much we love Jesus is shown by how much we love others.

SECTION OBJECTIVES

Review these objectives. When you have completed this section, you should be able to:

9. Explain why we should witness.
10. Describe Jesus' example of love.

Restudy these words.

adopt   glorify

 Read Psalm 139.

UNDERSTANDING YOURSELF

In order to understand yourself, you will have to see yourself as God sees you. In this section you will review how God made you and cares for you.

Many people say, "Believe in yourself and you can do anything." Starting with yourself is the wrong place to start. You need to start with God. Philippians 4:13 says "I can do all things through Christ which strengtheneth me." If you believe in Christ, you can do all things because He will give you the strength.

Wonderfully made. God made man different from all the other creatures. Man is very special to God. God made man in His own image. The parts of you which are most like God cannot be seen with the eye. You have a mind to understand, a heart to love, and a will to choose.

God made you with special abilities. As you grow older, you will use these special abilities more and more.

The Bible tells us that man was made to **glorify** God. When we believe in Him and obey His Word, we glorify God.

Unscramble these words and write them correctly on the lines.

lilw   tearh   dimn

3.1   to choose _____
3.2   to love _____
3.3   to understand _____
3.4   I love God with my _____ .
3.5   I can think about God with my _____ .
3.6   My _____ decides whether to do right or wrong.

Special to God. God sees you as you really are (sinful), or He sees you with Jesus in you (forgiven). If Jesus is in you, He has forgiven all the wrong things you have thought and done. God sees you as forgiven because Jesus takes away all your sin. God sees a forgiven person when He sees Jesus in you because Jesus paid for your sins.

Never boast about what you can do. God does not want you to see yourself as better than you are. Neither does He want you to feel worthless. He wants you to think about what you can do through Him or what He can do through you.

David did not boast about what he could do, but always told about what the Lord could do for him. Just before David killed the giant he said, "This day *will the LORD* deliver thee into my hand."

God wants you to see yourself as His child. God **adopted** you into His family when you received Jesus as your Savior. You are a child of God, you are part of an important family!

God has greater power than any

Sinner

Forgiven

ruler on earth ever had. Someday all people will bow down to Him. He will rule for ever and ever, and you shall rule with Him if you are His child.

By knowing God and studying His word, you will gain knowledge to understanding yourself. You must know God and who He is to understand your true worth.

👉 **Complete these statements.**

3.7   You can glorify God by _____ and obeying His Word.

3.8   Adopt means _____ .
                (If you forget, look in the vocabulary list.)

3.9   When you believed in Jesus, you were adopted into _____
_____ .

3.10   Knowing God is the first step to _____ .

3.11   Someday all people will bow down to _____ .

3.12   Man was made to _____ God.

3.13   "I can do all things through _____ ."

A verse is hidden in each box of letters. Find the place to begin and follow the trail to the end. Write the verse below each box.   The first one is done for you.

3.14

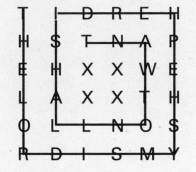

```
D L R O W E N
T V E D T H O
H O L O S D S
A F O R G O N
T H E G A V E
N O S I H E T
L Y B E G O T
```

<u>The Lord is my Shepherd,</u>

<u>I shall not want. Psalm 23:1</u>

_____

_____

3.15

```
U P M A L A
N T H G I S
T U H T L I
O N X A A D
M T X P D R
Y O M Y N O
F E E T A W
X X X T H Y
```

_____

_____

3.16

```
T A H T E
T H E L Y
H D R O W
E X K N O
I S G O D
```

_____

_____

 Read 1 Corinthians, Chapter 13.

REACHING OTHERS

After Jesus arose from the dead, He came back to talk with and comfort His friends. The last thing Jesus told His disciples to do was to go everywhere and preach the Gospel.

Jesus' command is for all of His disciples. You are Jesus' disciple if you have received Him as your Savior.

Tell the Gospel. Jesus told us to witness. He did not say we had to change people's hearts. He told us to tell the "Good News." God's Holy Spirit does the work of changing people. You can tell people what Jesus has done for you.

You can witness at all times and in all places. Do not wait for a better time or place to tell someone the Gospel. You may not have another chance.

Do you remember how Paul was changed by meeting Jesus? Right away Paul told others that Jesus is the Son of God. Do you remember how Andrew brought his brother, Peter, to Jesus after he first met Him? Andrew did not wait to tell Peter.

Jesus is now in heaven preparing a place for us. That is good news! Should we keep such wonderful news to ourselves?

 Write *true* **or** *false*.

3.17 _____ The last thing Jesus told His disciples was to go everywhere and preach the Gospel.

3.18 _____ Jesus has disciples today.

3.19 _____ God wants us to change people.

3.20 _____ You should never witness about Jesus on Sunday.

3.21 _____ Jesus wants you to witness.

Complete this verse by writing the right vowels on the lines.

3.22 "G __ y __ __ n t __ __ ll th __ w __ rld, __ nd pr __ __ ch th __ g __ sp __ l t __ __ v __ ry cr __ __ t __ r __ ." (Mark 16:15)

Match these items.

3.23 _____	proverb	a. the best way to begin Bible study
3.24 _____	prayer	b. wise saying
3.25 _____	principles	c. the only giver of life
3.26 _____	God	d. basic truths
3.27 _____	Genesis	e. tell us what to do or not to do
3.28 _____	commands	f. God wants us to seek this
3.29 _____	knowledge	g. story of Creation
3.30 _____	Canaan	h. a parable
		i. Holy Land

Show the love of Christ. The Bible is the story of how God loves and saves people. The Bible tells us that we must not only tell about the love of Christ, but we must show His love, too. Can you remember some ways you learned this year of showing Christ's love?

One of the best ways to show that you love God is by showing love to others.

People know us by our actions. A good way to tell others about Jesus is to act as He would act. People will not listen to our words about Jesus if we are always doing sinful things.

Jesus tells us that when we do for others we are really doing for Him. He mentions giving food to hungry people, clothing to the poor, and helping those who are sick.

Do you love your enemies? One of the hardest things to do is to love someone who has been unkind to you. Jesus set the perfect example of love. He loved and forgave the very people who killed Him.

Jesus said that you prove you are God's children when you return kind acts for unkindness. Following Jesus' example means being kind to all people and showing God's love to them.

Read and complete this verse.

3.31   "By this shall all men know that ye are my disciples, if you have _____ ." (John 13:35)

Complete this activity.

3.32   Are the children in these pictures showing love? _____

a.

b.

3.33   Write how these pictures would change if the children followed the verse in 3:31.

a. _____

_____

_____

_____

_____

_____

b. _____

_____

_____

_____

_____

Teacher check _____

                        Initial   Date

Think of someone who is not a Christian that you would like to show Christ's love to this next week.

3.34   Write his or her name here. _____

3.35   Now, think of three different ways you can show love to them this week.

a. _____

b. _____

c. _____

When this person becomes a Christian, come back to this page and put a star by the name.

      Before you take this last Self Test, you may want to do one or more of these self checks.

1. _____   Read the objectives. See if you can do them.

2. _____   Restudy the material related to any objectives that you cannot do.

3. _____ Use the SQ3R study procedure to review the material:
   a. **S**can the sections,
   b. **Q**uestion yourself,
   c. **R**ead to answer your questions,
   d. **R**ecite the answers to yourself, and
   e. **R**eview areas you did not understand.
4. _____ Review all vocabulary, activities, and Self Tests, writing a correct answer for every wrong answer.

SELF TEST 3

Complete these sentences with words from the list (each answer, 3 points).

love	yourself	will
Gospel	Epistles	God
Bible	heart	glorify
Christ	index	

3.01   I decide whether to do right or wrong with my _____ .

3.02   Man was made to _____ God.

3.03   "I can do all things through _____ which strengtheneth me."

3.04   Someday all people will bow down to _____ .

3.05   Knowing God is the first step to understanding _____

_____ .

3.06   Paul wrote thirteen _____ .

3.07   A word that means *good news* is _____ .

3.08   To find God's knowledge, we must look in the _____ .

Circle the letter of the words that complete these sentences (each answer, 4 points).

3.09   The last thing Jesus told His disciples was _____ .

a. go ye

b. love each other

c. come unto me

46

3.010   We should witness _____ .
a. only at home
b. only at church
c. everywhere

3.011   The only one who can change lives is the _____ .
a. doctors
b. Holy Spirit
c. law

3.012   "By this shall all men know that ye are my disciples, if ye
have _____ ."
a. love one to another
b. happiness
c. friends

3.013   The story of Saul meeting Jesus is found in _____ .
a. Mark
b. Romans
c. Acts

3.014   The shepherd of the Twenty-Third Psalm is _____ .
a. Paul
b. Jesus
c. Andrew

3.015   Reading the Bible is _____ .
a. difficult
b. spiritual food
c. silly

Write *true* **or** *false* (each answer, 2 points).

3.016 _____ Memorizing Scripture will clutter your mind.

3.017 _____ The Holy Spirit changed Saul from a hater to a lover.

3.018 _____ Scientists can make a human body.

3.019 _____ Paul had to suffer for Jesus.

3.020 _____ Scientists knew things before Bible writers.

3.021 _____ The greatest wonder God created is the sun.

3.022 _____ When we memorize Scripture, we should use these
steps: copy, read, say, tell, restudy.

3.023 _____ Paul wrote Proverbs.

3.024 _____ My worth comes from God.

Match these items (each answer, 2 points).

3.025 _____ fertile   a. Peter's brother

3.026 _____ Andrew   b. wrote Proverbs

3.027 _____ principles   c. basic truths

3.028 _____ Saul   d. rich

3.029 _____ David   e. Paul

3.030 _____ Solomon   f. wrote many Psalms

3.031 _____ a river   g. Jordan

Complete these verses (each answer, 4 points).

3.032   "Know ye that the Lord he is God: it is he that hath made us, and not we ourselves; we are his _____ ."

3.033   "But as many as received Him, to them gave He power to become the sons of God, even to them that _____ _____ ." (John 1:12)

3.034   "Surely goodness and mercy shall follow me all the days of my life: and I will _____ ." (Psalm 23:6)

3.035   "Go ye into all the world, and _____ _____ ." (Mark 16:15)

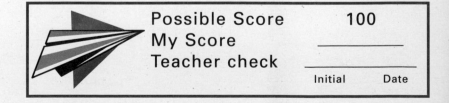

Possible Score	100
My Score	_____
Teacher check	_____
	Initial Date

Before taking the LIFEPAC Test, you may want to do one or more of these self checks.

1. _____ Read the objectives. See if you can do them.
2. _____ Restudy the material related to any objectives that you cannot do.
3. _____ Use the SQ3R study procedure to review the material.
4. _____ Review activities, Self Tests, and LIFEPAC vocabulary words.
5. _____ Restudy areas of weakness indicated by the last Self Test.

NOTES